To Santi

With Every
Best Wish,

H. Totten

The Art of Human Care

HASSAN A. TETTEH
with ELLA BLEUE

Inquiries about this book should be addressed to:
TCG Publishing
Bethesda, Maryland, USA
(800) 838-7061

www.doctortetteh.com

The Art of Human Care
Hassan A. Tetteh
with Ella Bleue
ISBN: 978-1-7336654-2-1
Library of Congress Control Number: 2019910302

Written by Hassan A. Tetteh
Cover Design by Steven Dana & Karen McDiarmid | Book Design by Karen McDiarmid
Illustrated by Jessica Legon & Ella Bleue

Printed in Canada

10 9 8 7 6 5 4 3 2 1

for

Amy Saad Tetteh

Ars longa, vita brevis.

—Hippocrates

Translation:
Art is long, life is short.

Contents

Foreword...7
by Dr. E. Thomas Moran

Introduction 13

Part I
Genesis of *The Art of Human Care*..23

Part II
Introduction to *The Art of Human Care* Theory................................39

The Art of Human Care in Action: Purpose
A Love of a Lifetime 41

The Art of Human Care in Action: Personalization
Unbiased Care 47

The Art of Human Care in Action: Partnership
How a Team Rallies Together to Save a Life.....................................53

Part III
A Call to Action:
How to Change the World One Patient at a Time..............................59

The Art of Human Care in Action: Purpose
The Healing Effect of a Smile..63

The Art of Human Care in Action: Personalization
Never Underestimate the Potential of Your Patients.........................67

The Art of Human Care in Action: Partnership
A Miracle in the Desert...74

Afterword 79

Acknowledgments...81

POURING HEARTS: Jessica Legon

Foreword

Dr. E. Thomas Moran

The idea for this book is, quite literally, beautiful. Dr. Hassan Tetteh has combined the beauty of art—with its unrestrained love of color and connection to a rich inner emotional life—with the beauty of compassion—the openness to caring connections with other human beings. Both art and compassion grace the human experience and reveal the best that is in us.

The idea of combining his lifelong commitment to human compassion with his young daughter Ella's artwork is, in many respects, a natural expression of the meaning of Dr. Tetteh's life.

I have known Dr. Tetteh since the early 1990s when he was an undergraduate at the State University of New York at Plattsburgh. At the time, I was serving as provost of the college. As a student, Hassan displayed exceptional academic and leadership qualities. Instead of merely being inspired by his teachers, he also inspired them. He has gone on in life to have one of the most extraordinary careers of any person I have ever known.

From early on, it was clear that Hassan wanted to live a meaningful life in which serving others was a central dynamic. Near the end of his undergraduate career, he debated whether to go to medical school and become a healer or, as one of his most revered mentors suggested, apply to the John F. Kennedy School of Government at Harvard University and affect the world through public policy. He eventually did both.

After completing his undergraduate career, he went on to receive his medical degree from Downstate Medical Center in New York City. His next move—enlisting to serve in the United States Navy—was somewhat surprising and equally admirable.

Dr. Tetteh was born soon after his family arrived in the United States from Ghana in West Africa. He felt that he and his family had been fortunate to be able to come here—and that they owed a great deal to this country. Consequently, he enlisted. He remains an active duty officer with the rank of captain. He served as the chief medical informatics officer (CMIO) at Navy Medicine's Headquarters in Washington, D.C., and as an associate professor of surgery at the Uniformed Services University of the Health Sciences.

During the Iraq War, Hassan served as the ship's surgeon on the USS *Carl Vinson*. After that, he received and completed a prestigious fellowship in cardiothoracic surgery at the University of Minnesota. Since that time, as a board certified general and thoracic surgeon, he has performed heart-lung transplant surgeries in this highly demanding field.

He and I remained close during these years. In fact, after his father passed away, we became even closer. One winter night more than a decade ago, as he approached graduation from his fellowship at the University of Minnesota, he called me and asked if I would come to his graduation in the spring. He told me that it would mean the world to him if I could be there. I told him that I was honored that he had asked me and certainly intended to attend. However, that spring when his graduation neared, fate intervened in an unexpected way. The day after one of my usual Sunday afternoon eight-mile power walks, I went to get the results of what my doctors and I were sure would be a routine test. Instead, I was told that I needed quadruple heart bypass surgery. I would have to miss Hassan's graduation. So, a few days later, he flew back to the East Coast to be with me when I had the surgery, a procedure that he had just completed preparation and training to perform. That following year, he did go to the Harvard Kennedy School where he received a master's degree in public administration. I was able to be there on that proud day.

I so much appreciated his trip to be with me and my family when I was in the hospital. This extraordinary gesture of support, coming as it did at such a busy time in his own life, is characteristic of his almost inherent generosity of spirit and compassion.

Before Hassan left the hospital, he left me a beautiful letter. He signed it with the phrase, "With the adoration of a son." I wrote back to him and signed my letter, "With the pride of a father." Throughout the years, we have written to each other often, including during his many travels and painfully arduous deployment. We always sign our letters with these special closings.

In 2011, Hassan was deployed to Afghanistan as a combat trauma surgeon in a Role 2, Forward Resuscitative Surgical Suite field hospital. He treated U.S. Marines, many of whom had been devastatingly wounded in battle. His posting was particularly poignant for me. During World War II, my father had served in the Marine Corps. Navy doctors provide care to sick and wounded Marines. In a way, Hassan's deployment seemed to complete a private circle of care between the two men whom I admired most in my life.

Upon returning from overseas duty, Hassan received a highly prestigious fellowship from the Robert Wood Johnson Foundation. He was assigned to the U.S. Congressional Budget Office (CBO) to work on health care policy as a visiting scholar. Before this time, he had also completed a master's in business administration at Johns Hopkins University where his interests focused on medical finance, information, and technology.

In 2016, Hassan was appointed Command Surgeon for the National Defense University, War College, in Washington, D.C. He subsequently studied for and received a master's degree in national security strategy, with a focus on artificial intelligence from the National War College.

In addition to his professional life as a Naval Officer and medical doctor, he is active in voluntary public service. For example, among other activities, Dr. Tetteh serves on the boards of the Arthur Ashe Institute for Urban Health Care; Champions for Kids, based in Fayetteville, Arkansas; and Miriam's Kitchen, a Washington, D.C.–based organization that works to end homelessness. Even though Hassan is a quiet person, he is phenomenally energetic. With all that his daily schedule requires, he still finds time to run marathons to raise money for charity organizations! Additionally, he has written both professional articles and two inspiring novels titled *Gifts of the Heart* and *Star Patrol*.

That circle of care continues in his life. Since early childhood, my older daughter has been best friends with a young woman who has cystic fibrosis. They have been almost like sisters for 35 years. In the past year, her friend's health grew perilous. It was clear that, without a lung transplant, she would not have long to live. Suddenly and almost miraculously, the opportunity for that lifesaving operation materialized. My daughter traveled immediately to the hospital in Washington D.C., to be with her friend. Within hours, we learned of the doctor who had been instrumental in this lifesaving operation. His name was Dr. Hassan Tetteh.

Hassan has a lovely wife, Lisa, and two beautiful children. He is deeply and lovingly engaged in their lives. This is another more personal example of not only the extraordinary energy but also the wise balance he displays in his life. His daughter's artwork inspired this book.

I have tried here to explain something of Hassan's personality and to highlight his extraordinary career. It confirms, I hope, the intelligence and commitment that he possesses. What these facts of his life cannot entirely convey, however, is a portrait of his character. He is obviously an exceptionally talented and deeply committed person, but he is also profoundly humane, humble, decent, and caring. His story of arising out of a humble background, remarkable accomplishments, and the dignity and devotion with which he lives his life exemplify the very best qualities that human beings can exhibit—qualities that this society most hopes for in its leading citizens.

Perhaps even more importantly, it is essential to recognize that greatness in a society depends on its capacity to cultivate and respect compassion, to appreciate beauty in art, and to realize that those two capacities are bound together in the human spirit. This book aspires to remind us of this fundamental insight.

E. Thomas Moran, PhD
Distinguished Service Professor Emeritus
State University of New York at Plattsburgh

DYING HEARTS: Jessica Legon

Introduction

Hassan A. Tetteh

I wanted to be an artist when I grew up. I loved art. As a child growing up in the 1970s and 1980s in the small village/town of Brooklyn, I contributed to the graffiti mosaic that appeared vividly on trains carrying the masses to and from their destinations throughout New York's five boroughs. My immigrant father's prudent, if not entirely practical, wisdom curtailed my burgeoning art career. When I was accepted by New York City's Art and Design High School—a testament to my early artistic talent and high regard for my cherished art portfolio—my father would not let me enroll. He rationalized that I would never make money as an artist. He insisted, and only approved, my attending Brooklyn Technical High School, a specialized science and engineering school that required an entrance exam for admission. Perhaps my father helped me make the right decision. As a child born of immigrant parents from poor African countries, my aspiration to be an artist was a luxury neither my family nor I could afford. Ultimately, I became a doctor and surgeon.

However, I still love art. *The Art of Human Care* is now my life's work.

As a first-generation African American, I've endured many of the challenges associated with that identity. I fully understand how being African American, particularly with African immigrant parents, shaped my worldview. Often forgoing their own dreams and aspirations, my parents sacrificed much to make an investment in me. Therefore, they expected much of me.

My name, Hassan, always gave me a bit of a complex. While I was growing up, many of my friends made fun of my name because it was different. Though a common name in the Middle East, in today's xenophobic climate, my name evokes all kinds of judgments from others. I was named Hassan after my mother's Lebanese father, a businessman living in Sierra Leone, West Africa, my mother's birthplace. My father was from Accra, Ghana. As my father's parents had done for him, my parents sent me to a Catholic school, Holy Family, an elementary and middle school in Canarsie, Brooklyn. I was consequently indoctrinated into Catholicism. After a brief academic detour in ninth grade to Meyer Levin, a public middle school, I began a busy high school career at Brooklyn Technical High School. After graduation, I attended a small arts and science college in upstate New York, the State University of New York College at Plattsburgh.

In surgery, we abruptly alter the natural course of our patient's disease by applying the scalpel's cold, hard steel. We induce trauma to change our patients' lives, ideally for the better. Ultimately, as an undergrad, a near-death experience and traumatic tragedy set in motion the series of events that would determine the course of my life.

Being a "Patient"

As a pre-med student in college, I interviewed at Johns Hopkins Medical School under an early decision program. I was beyond excited. After my interview, I knew I was destined to become a doctor. I returned to my small college in upstate New York to await the official news of my acceptance. Over the ensuing days, I became very ill with fever, chills, and the worst headache and neck pain of my life. I visited our college infirmary, was diagnosed (incorrectly) with gastroenteritis, prescribed penicillin tablets, and instructed to stay in bed and drink plenty of fluids. My condition worsened. On a Friday night, I was alone in my dorm room and unable to call for help. Thankfully, two worried fraternity brothers came into my room to check on me.

When they found me, I was lethargic and barely responsive. They rushed me to the local hospital emergency room. I recall bright lights and masked people hovering over me, sternal rubs, and being told to hold still because a needle was going into my back. The doctor told me that I had a severe infection and could die.

I was a patient.

Many people experience being a patient in their lives, but not to this extreme. You are truly a patient when you are stripped of your own clothes, wear the hospital-issued gown in humiliation, can no longer do anything for yourself, and have no idea what is going on. That happened to me. I did not understand what was happening. I was uncertain, anxious, and scared. I thought I was going to die.

Fortunately, my healing mind took over and did what medicine alone could not have done. Engendered by my recent interview for medical school, my spirited soul believed that I was destined to become a healer.

This gave me a positive outlook on my future. After all, I had interviewed at Johns Hopkins! I was determined that an infection wouldn't take me out. My own subsequent healing process helped me to appreciate the power of thought, the mind, and how a positive, optimistic vision of a future purpose could impact health.

During my near-death experience as a college junior, I was at once faced with two realities. One, I had been given a second chance at life. Two, I appreciated and found the answer to a simple question with great urgency: Why am I still alive? Contracting a lethal bacterial meningitis infection and then experiencing a delay in diagnosis delivered an otherwise fit, healthy, and invincible teenager to the intensive care unit where a tube was inserted into every body orifice. Only after emerging from my ordeal did I learn that the experts had issued a poor prognosis. Every statistic suggested I would die. The odds were against me. Yet I lived.

That fateful time during undergrad abruptly altered the natural course of my life. I've spent my life reconciling two realities. I was given a second chance at life so there must be a reason why. Some time later, I learned that Johns Hopkins would not accept me to medical school as I had so intensely desired.

Although many years have passed since my near-death ordeal, I still remember the lessons learned about human care that being a patient taught me. My experience taught me about empathy—and what it feels like to be a patient. The average physician has an average of 80,000 to 100,000 patient encounters over a typical career. Thus, potentially 100,000 patients like me could share about the impact their health care encounter had on their lives. Not all battles are as involved as mine were. However, in my own career, I realize that the work we do in health care engenders incredible power and offers equally incredible gifts. We significantly impact lives and, consequently, change the world.

I am a healer. On numerous occasions, including when I learned the disappointing news from Johns Hopkins, I tried to run away from this fact. With some regret, I also reflected on my abandoned aspiration to be an artist. In the process, an epiphany emerged. The art of healing through surgery was my singular purpose—it is still the reason I believe I'm here. I survived death to be a healer. When I say "healer," I mean physically, spiritually, and emotionally. My work in heart and lung transplantation repeatedly and viscerally exposes me to life's fragility—the physical reality of death. With every case, the reward and miracle of life that a transplant brings to a desperately ill recipient restores my optimism in the ethereal. My greatest satisfaction and joy come from helping others. Through performing surgery, providing inspiration, and sharing challenges I've overcome in my own life that align with another's story, I offer hope for the possible.

Physicians Can Heal without Curing

The Art of Human Care is my prescription for the health care system's focus on sick-care rather than health and wellness. It is a remedy for our inherent dissatisfaction with health care. At the hospital, people need more than sick-care to experience true healing. Instead of feeling worse after engaging with our health care system, they can discover that they have a purpose. By identifying their purpose, an individual can come alive and feel invigorated, even with a terminal illness. I have seen it. I've seen people go from knocking on death's door to turning their lives around and living fully with purpose, passion, and vigor. Achieving health is our real goal—and it does not have to cost a lot. True health and subjective well-being come from someplace else. Typically, from a patient's support system—friends, family, community, church, or others—not from the health care system.

I would argue that to achieve health through human care, patients need to connect to a purpose beyond their hospitalization. We all need a purpose. With purpose comes renewed life. For a patient, purpose transcends anything we, as providers, can give them in the hospital. A study of the ancient models of healing reveals healers who really healed. Healers who studied the whole body and appreciated the totality of an individual's relationships, existence, and experiences. These healers would note what contributed to a patient's ill health and observe when the body was out of balance. Today, despite our sophisticated diagnostics, we only assess a patient's purpose in a cursory way. In this context, how much information do we obtain in our traditional settings? How much do patients reveal during a hurried office visit, the fleeting moment during hospital inpatient rounds, or in the bustling pace of an emergency room? To appreciate a patient's challenges in a meaningful way, let alone understand the patient's purpose in order to address their needs, we need a different approach. This type of purpose-led care rarely happens in our current settings. Yet, critical insight into a patient's purpose—and delivery of human care—absolutely impacts a person's health.

Changing the World

The Art of Human Care aims to change the world. Like our surgical example of cold, hard steel altering the natural course of one's disease and problems, *The Art of Human Care* alters the natural course of health care as we know it today. This book presents the art in three sections.

The first section, "The Genesis of *The Art of Human Care*," shares a summary of a White Coat Ceremony keynote address I delivered to the class of 2018 at my alma mater, State University of New York, Downstate Medical Center, College of Medicine. It was an honor to be chosen to address the newest generation of healers. In preparing to inspire the talented physicians-to-be, I thought critically about what it means to heal. I presented my vision of how to change the world through healing. It was well received by the medical students.

The second section, "Human Care Theory," represents an evolution of thought shaped and inspired by mentors, teachers, readings, science, and engagements with my patients. This section seeks to distill human care into an actionable and teachable art form that includes the "3 P's": finding Purpose, Personalization, and Partnerships.

The third section, "A Call to Action: Change the World," is a summary of the keynote I delivered to the Fairfield County Medical Association, a cadre of Master Physician Honorees and members of the country's oldest medical society during its 224th annual meeting.

Throughout *The Art of Human Care*, I've infused inspired, original art, illustrated hearts from my daughter, Ella Bleue, and made reference to my own challenges of loss, sacrifice, death, and redemption. Reflection on my experience as a surgeon and aspiring artist confirms that art is not merely an escape from work but necessary for providing the energy and inspiration to do work even better. Thus, art helps make the work of healing better. I've observed its positive effect on patients during healing arts exhibits. I am not alone in this observation. In our places of healing and health, art is both ubiquitous on the walls and displayed in sculptures. Music often fills the air. Art heals and, indeed, is a gift for the heart. As my daughter, the artist, admonishes, without "art" the heart is just "eh."

As a transplant surgeon, my work places me on both sides of the continuum of life. At the donor's bedside, tragedy takes away life while giving life to someone else in need. Decisions for donor families are often hard. The finality signals that hope for recovery has been vanquished. Sadness, grief, and loss are often omnipresent. At the recipient's bedside, emotions are high with joy, anxiety, and anticipation. Desperately ill patients waiting for a transplant feel familiar with their mortality at the fringe of life. They seldom waste a moment brooding over petty concerns. Similar to performing complex surgery, writing a book, and particularly a creative work, engenders great humility. Thus, *The Art of Human Care* is offered, devoid of hubris, to contribute and serve others in the critical work of achieving and sustaining health.

While *The Art of Human Care* represents the totality of my medical career, it also combines the healing power of art and science as well as inspired keynotes delivered to both new and seasoned generations of healers. I have sought to create an evolving work with the singular aim of healing individuals and positively changing the world.

SHAMAN: Jessica Legon

HIPPOCRATES: Jessica Legon

Part I

Genesis of *The Art of Human Care*

A few years ago, I presented research at the meeting of the World Society of Cardiothoracic Surgeons in Kos, Greece. This trip inspired a very important part of my work in *The Art of Human Care* and how to be a healer. The acronym **LEARN,** described later in this chapter, will summarize what I learned on the last day of my trip to Greece when I visited the famed Asclepius Temple of Kos. More than 2,300 years ago, Hippocrates received his medical training in Kos. As I stood at the very spot at the top of the Temple steps where Nikias had stood centuries ago, I imagined going back in time to the year 399 B.C. where his story—a story that continues to inspire my work—took place.

The Story of Hippocrates

When Nikias, a young businessman, felt a great pain in his chest, he became very concerned. He was 39 years old. He remembered that his father had a similar pain in his chest immediately before he collapsed and died at the age of 40. Nikias' grandfather had also died under the same circumstances at the age of 40.

Nikias summoned his son. Together, they made their way by oxen-cart to the healers at the Temple of Asclepius. As Nikias slowly climbed the many stairs to the Temple entrance, he clutched his heart. By the time he reached the top step and knocked on the large Temple doors, he was completely out of breath.

From the top of the stairs, Nikias spied a very distinguished man dressed in white, tending to poor beggars outside of the Temple. Before he could hail the man, the Temple doors swung open, and one of the Temple priests greeted Nikias, who shared that he had a pain in his chest and was seeking help. The priest rattled off the high sum that Nikias would be required to pay before entering the great healing Temple of Asclepius. The hefty sum was as steep as the stairs Nikias had just climbed. Because the pain was getting worse, he agreed to pay.

When he entered the Temple, Nikias was in awe of its fine marble interior. "This healing must be good business," he thought to himself.

After the priest assured Nikias that he would receive the best of care, he took Nikias' clothes and gave him a robe. The priest told him that, to keep his body pure, he could neither eat food nor drink water. This would ensure that during his dreams, Nikias would receive a visitation delivering the message for his cure.

As the priest made his sacrifices to the gods, Nikias noticed the many dogs and snakes in the Temple. Although the priests explained that snakes and dogs kept the demons away—and snake bites can cure illness—Nikias was not totally convinced.

In the morning, after a long, restless, noisy night interrupted by all kinds of disturbances in the Temple, Nikias was awakened by the Temple priests. When they asked Nikias about his dreams, he had nothing to report. The priests shook their heads in sad disappointment. After all, Nikias' dreams had not revealed the cure for his illness.

Nikias left the Temple in deep frustration. After two days of being subjected to the "best medical care available," of experiencing all that the priests could do for him in 399 B.C, the pain still throbbed in his chest. After making the weary walk back down the Temple's many steps, Nikias collapsed. Lying on his back at the bottom of the Temple stairs, Nikias looked up to see the man dressed in white, whom he'd first noticed the day he arrived at the Temple. The man told Nikias that he was a doctor and that he would help him. Nikias protested at first. He asked the man, "If you are a doctor, why aren't you practicing in the healing Temple?" The man replied, "Oh, they don't practice my kind of medicine in the Temple."

The man helped Nikias into his humble healing place. The doctor's place was clean—no snakes or dogs! Furthermore, his calm and caring manner comforted Nikias and inspired his trust. The doctor proceeded to ask Nikias many questions about his family, the nature of his pain, what he ate, how he slept, and how hard he worked. The Temple priests never asked any of these questions.

Next, the doctor thoroughly examined Nikias. He placed his hand on Nikias' neck, then on his wrist to check his pulse. He looked down Nikias' throat and stared deeply into his eyes. After his examination, the good doctor explained, "You have blocked vessels here (pointing below Nikias' collar bone) and here (pointing to the center of his chest). Your body is out of balance. Your heart is not healthy. If it gets worse, you will lose your ability to move, and you will eventually die."

Nikias asked the doctor, "What can I do?"

The doctor responded, "First, you must change your diet, no meat or milk, nothing that thickens your blood. You must eat plenty of oranges and lemons. Second, you must rest!"

Nikias laughed and asked, "Who has time to rest?"

The doctor responded, "If you do not do these things, you will die."

The doctor took Nikias' arm and made a small cut to let blood flow into a bowl. After having drawn enough blood, he announced that balance had been restored.

Indeed, Nikias returned home feeling better than he had in a long time. He continued to follow the doctor's advice. Weeks later, the great Temple of Asclepius was badly damaged in a fire. Rumors swirling throughout the city of Kos named Hippocrates the physician as responsible for burning down the Temple! Nikias determined that the doctor who treated him was this same Hippocrates—he never forgot this doctor or his name.

How It Relates to Medicine Today

Hippocrates built on medical knowledge that he had gleaned from the ancient Egyptians to become the "father of modern medicine." Those who studied under Hippocrates and other ancient doctors ushered in an era of scientific inquiry, organized knowledge, and the art of diagnosis and healing.

After my visit to the Temple, I traveled a short distance across Kos to the center of town. There, the Tree of Hippocrates grows, the place where he purportedly taught his students. I liberated a leaf from the tree and saved it as a reminder of what I had learned during my experience on Kos.

What does the story of Nikias and Hippocrates have to do with the practice of medicine today? How can a story from 2,300 years ago relate to the 21st century? Well, the beginnings of modern medicine more than two millennia ago changed the world. The practice of modern medicine can continue to change the world when we don't stray too far from the roots of that ancient tree.

Consider this. When I graduated from Downstate in 1998, Downstate's Dr. Fruchgott was awarded the Noble Prize in Medicine for his research on nitric oxide. In 1998, Facebook, Google, Twitter, and Instagram didn't exist. Students doing research before 1998 had to use the Dewy Decimal System. For endless hours, we searched in books in the library for some pearl of wisdom or answers to questions. Today, students can simply "google it."

Lessons I learned growing up on the streets of Brooklyn, serving in the military, and listening to the wisdom of my teachers and mentors provided more pearls of wisdom. And the many people I have been honored to care for over my brief medical career have taught me the most.

It does not matter where you grew up or if you served in uniform. The lessons I learned are universal. They apply to all of us, no matter what our gender, ethnicity, religion, orientation, or social status.

For all healers, the struggles and challenges are similar. The goal is not only to heal but also to teach the next generation of healers. What does it mean to heal? It means to restore health. Why is health so important? Because without health, nothing else matters as much.

I was reminded of this fact during my time as a cardiothoracic surgery fellow in Minnesota. The brutal Midwest winter finally got the best of me. One day, I was feeling especially miserable and unhealthy. I went to work and made my way to the student center infirmary. CT surgery fellows were not allowed sick days. We lived by the mantra, "You are either in the hospital working or you are in the hospital as a patient."

On my way to the infirmary, I stopped at a large wall that I had passed many times before. The wall was inscribed with a message. However, this was the first time I actually acknowledged the large words boldly written there, words that were both sobering and immediately relevant to my condition. "When health is absent, wisdom cannot reveal itself, art cannot manifest, strength cannot fight, wealth becomes useless, and intelligence cannot be applied."

The words on the wall quoted Herophilus of Chalcedon, physician to Alexander the Great and pupil of Hippocrates. Herophilus, also a great teacher in his era, understood what health meant. His words helped me realize that in order to change the world, physicians needed to not only heal the people they care for but also teach the next generation of healers to do the same.

The lessons I learned prescribe how to take care of patients, how to be a healer, and how to teach the next generation of healers. They can be embodied in the acronym **LEARN**: listen, empathize, affinitize, repeat, and (know) the now.

LEARN TO LISTEN: Jessica Legon

LEARN
LISTEN

In order to heal Nikias, Hippocrates first listened to him. He asked about his father and his father's father (family history). He asked what Nikias ate and what he did for a living (lifestyle choices). The doctor heard Nikias. In our first year of medical school at Downstate, Dr. Friedman admonished that if we listen to the patient, truly listen to the patient, "They will tell you the diagnosis." This has proved true every time I've truly listened to my patient.

If, as a physician, you want to change the world, you must listen to your patients—really listen to them.

lEarn
EMPATHIZE

My "death bed" experience as a patient in the ICU taught me about empathy. I know what it feels like to be a patient. *If, as a physician, you want to change the world, you must empathize with your patients and what they are experiencing. You must imagine walking in their shoes.* This will help you to better understand their pain and situation.

Oftentimes, when physicians prescribe a course of therapy for their patients, they use metrics and jargon they are comfortable with. It seems to work well for communicating while practicing in the medical profession. For example, HgbA1C, low 30-day mortality, and no ventilator associated pneumonias are fair measures of outcome that we take great pride in. However, these words and medical measures may not mean much to our patients.

leArn
AFFINITIZE

What means even more is when a physician learns to affinitize with the patient when describing the treatment and plan of care. In fact, this is what matters most to the patient. If a patient comes to a physician complaining of shortness of breath, says he loves to hunt with his buddies, and specifically complains that he cannot go hunting anymore because he can't breathe, what plan of care will the physician put in place? Prescribe an echocardiogram? When the echo study finds mild aortic stenosis, send him to surgery and fix his valve? Get him out of the hospital in four days without a 30-day complication? That will all look good on the books. However, if the physician neglects to address the issue that upsets the patient—he can't go hunting with his buddies anymore—and instead provides only procedural success, the physician has failed. If, as a result of the procedure, the patient's shortness of breath is even worse, the physician has done little to address what was most important to the patient.

If, as a physician, you want to change the world, you must affinitize with the patient through your plan of care. Make sure your advice and treatment address what matters most to the patient.

LEARN
REPEAT

Consider, when they hear your advice, patients are under a great deal of stress. It may take some reinforcement to really drive a point home. Repetition is important.

If, as a physician, you want to change the world, you must repeat the plan of care. Repeat it to the patient, and repeat it again to the family members. Make sure the lines of communication are clear and that all questions and concerns are answered.

LEARN
KNOW THE NOW

It is important to know what the patient's greatest current concern is. For example, nearly all physicians will encounter a patient with poorly controlled diabetes. After providing the best treatment, many wonder why the patient is noncompliant and why her sugar is always out of control. The physician routinely will blame the patient for not following instructions.

However, if the physician listens to the patient, she or he may discover that the patient has challenges in getting her medications from the pharmacy. The physician must find ways to help her overcome the challenges—while increasing her motivation to overcome them, as well. Perhaps after a brief conversation, the physician learns that the patient's greatest joy in life is playing with her grandchildren. By helping the patient make the connection between lower HgbA1C and quality time with her grandchildren, the treatment plan becomes more meaningful. The physician could explain that if she doesn't control her sugar by eating right and taking her medications, she will not be around much longer. Doesn't she want to be there for her grandchild's graduation from high school, college, and medical school?

The patient may not care about a HgbA1C and she may not even understand what it is, but she will do whatever it takes to love and care for her grandchildren—now, and in the future.

If, as a physician, you want to change the world, you must know what the patient's concern is now. You can't rely on the chart or the computer screen, which tends to set up a roadblock to real conversation. Remember, the answer will only come from the patient.

The lessons outlined above admonish you to L—E—A—R—N: Listen, empathize, affinitize, repeat, and (know) the now.

Listen to the patient. Empathize with them. Affinitize with them. Repeat your plan of care. And get to know the now—learn what is important to this individual patient in this exact moment. By following these steps, you will, indeed, find the diagnosis, discover ways to help, heal the patient, and, ultimately, change the world.

As a new surgical intern, I took care of an elderly, Russian-speaking man with terminal stomach cancer. His cancer was unresectable, his disease very advanced, and he was not expected to live much longer.

He spoke no English. I spoke no Russian. I examined him every day. I learned about what he needed through interpreters and his family—he had a large family and many grandchildren. Even though he was often in pain and probably knew that he was going to die soon, I learned his greatest joy came when he visited with his family. When they came to see him, his face lit up the room.

One night while on call, I received a message that he was not doing well. It was very late, after visiting hours. His family had left for the evening. When I arrived in his room, he was unstable. It was clear he was living his final moments.

As a new, inexperienced, and anxious intern, I didn't know what to do. I turned to one of the senior nurses for help and instructions. She said, "Dr. Tetteh, call his family." As soon as I heard her words, I knew it was brilliant advice.

I called his family to explain that they needed to come right away. He was dying. Then, I worked with the nurses and team to stabilize him until his family arrived. When he passed away, he was comfortable and surrounded by his family. As he was one of my first patients to die while I was on call, I felt horrible. But despite how badly I felt, his family thanked me and was very grateful they were there during his final moments.

Changing the World

If, as a physician, you want to change the world, you must realize that death is not an option. Everyone will naturally die. What you do with your time here on earth, in service to others, is what matters most.

It's all about exceeding expectations. Healers must aim to exceed expectations with every patient encounter, even when they face challenges. When a physician asks what they can do to help others, even when hope seems fleeting, they exceed expectations.

In the 1940s, a Jewish psychiatrist imprisoned in the Auschwitz concentration camp, was assigned number 114108. Though he expected to die, he provided hope to his fellow prisoners since they were still alive. He even quoted Nietzsche, "Das was uns nich merken was staker totet," which translates, "That which does not kill you makes you stronger." Dr. Viktor Frankl, number 114108, survived his ordeal, provided hope to many he cared for, and gave the world the book *Man's Search for Meaning*.

If, as a physician, you want to change the world, you must know that you will face challenges. Learn to use them as opportunities—and help your patients to do the same. Give your patients hope even when it seems like none is available.

If, as a physician, you want to change the world, be grateful to all the people who have helped you along the way. Physicians must have gratitude for the awesome opportunity they have before them. Write to your teachers, mentors, and people who have helped you throughout life. Let them know how you are doing. Show and tell them how you are enjoying the fruit of their labor and support. You are someone's favorite unfolding story.

Yes, you can change the world! Commit yourself to being a healer and to teaching the next generation of healers. As a global community, physicians impact the lives of millions through the work that they do. You, personally, no matter what your specialty, will help mothers, fathers, teachers, children, the rich, and the poor.

Be a great healer. Teach the next generation of healers. Think LEARN—listen, empathize, affinitize, repeat, and (know) the now. Inspire hope, even when it seems that none is available. Be forever grateful for the opportunity you have each day to impact the lives of those who place their trust, their faith, and their lives in your care. And, when you remember those who helped you along the way, take a minute to tell them, "Thank you for the privilege you have made possible for me."

Human Care Theory

DR. HASSAN A. TETTEH, M.D.

WHAT is Human Care?
Human Care is timely, comprehensive care that advances each person's total health in body, mind and spirit.

WHAT problems does Human Care address?
Human Care challenges the current system that is not patient-centered and that is perpetuating fragmented care, escalating costs, and inefficient delivery.

WHY is Human Care important?
Human Care produces a healthier society by meeting the patient's need for real care, the physician's desire to be a true healer, and the country's want of actual value for dollars spent on healthcare.

PURPOSE

Revive Your Healing Passion
Resurrect your commitment to the honorable and meaningful purpose of helping people feel better.

Realize Your Healing Power
Grasp the impact you make as you restore people's health so they can realize their purpose and continue the chain reaction of changing the world.

PERSONALIZATION

Discover Your Patient's Present
Learn your patient's current state of being, including their values, dreams, and gifts for the world.

Maximize Your Patient Encounters
Capitalize on each interaction to create trust and the respectful connection that can change the world.

PARTNERSHIP

Leverage Your Team Dream
Advance the collective care team effort to achieve a total health impact for all.

Shape Your Professional Horizon
Create your unique legacy to elevate and unify the healthcare community for a lasting impact on health and humanity.

CONCRETE RESULTS

- The antidote for burnout in healthcare
- A new perspective on what it means to heal
- A formula that delivers a new level of healing
- The ideal model for providing effective care
- A passion to make healthcare great again

Part II

Introduction to
The Art of Human Care Theory

Three key elements comprise "human care":

- Purpose
- Personalization
- Partnerships

Purpose

When you ask an individual the abstract question, "What is your purpose?", they may find it difficult to answer. When you ask them the broader question, "Why are you alive?", you encourage them to think of something specific. It's an easier question for them to process in their mind. Purpose is more challenging. Finding purpose is not something that happens automatically by sitting and thinking about it. People almost always discover their purpose when they do something for someone else. It is in doing that "something" that they find their purpose.

I've said my purpose is to heal. Initially, I had a vague notion of what I wanted to do. As I helped people and received positive feedback, my work contributed to their health and well-being. In those actions, I found my purpose. Now, I'm passionate about healing. This is how it works with teachers, artists, and people in almost any profession. In the process of serving or doing something for others, individuals find their purpose. True purpose comes from serving others.

Purpose:
A Love of a Lifetime

Purpose is found in service to others. And who knows? Through service to others and in finding purpose, you may also find your love of a lifetime.

My first case as a surgical intern was like any other surgical case in medical school—but with one big difference. Now, unlike my time in medical school, I was a "doctor." I was responsible for patients' lives.

My first patient as a surgical intern was Mrs. DV. She was a wonderful woman. Unfortunately, she was very sick and chronically ill from end-stage renal disease (failure of her kidneys). A long history of chronic disease related to diabetes, high blood pressure, and other ailments sapped Mrs. DV's strength, weakened her body, and often stole her joy.

When she was presented to us for surgery, I was an intern working for the Chief of the Surgery Service at our hospital. As the first rotation of the year for all of the interns in our program, it was an honor to be the intern on the Chief of Surgery's Service— appropriately called the "A-Team." With honor, however, came responsibilities. The rotation was the most difficult and challenging experience of our entire five-year surgical residency. Our Chief of Surgery expected and demanded excellence. There were well-known stories of surgical interns that wouldn't make it, were dismissed from the program, and others who were never given the opportunity to serve on the Chief's service. As the A-Team surgical intern, one had to go above and beyond in every single action. Our Surgical Chief demanded his patients receive the very best care, and the entire machine of the hospital worked toward that end, especially his surgical intern.

I learned much from our Chief and wanted to be like him. Being on the A-Team was an invaluable way to begin my surgical career and I aimed to give the very best care to my patients at all times.

Mrs. DV was to be my first patient—and my first lesson. By design, Mrs. DV would become the "gold standard" for my patient care experience as a real doctor, emulating the actions, fine examples, and standard of excellence our Chief of Surgery demonstrated on a daily basis. I did not want to disappoint him. Mrs. DV suffered from tertiary hyperparathyroidism. As a consequence of her chronic end stage renal disease, Mrs. DV's parathyroid gland developed autonomous (unregulated) function of the gland, leading to serious life-threatening increased serum calcium levels. Mrs. DV did not respond to medical therapy and needed her abnormal parathyroid glands surgically removed. The surgical procedure was very delicate, demanded careful planning and precise attention to detail. There was no room for error. There are major blood vessels in the neck, and there were critical nerves in close proximity to the parathyroid tumors. As the abnormal parathyroid tumors were removed, the surrounding blood vessels and nerves needed to be spared. As the intern, there was not much for me to do during the procedure other than hold retractors and watch our Chief of Surgery in action. He was a master surgeon. I hoped by osmosis his skills would transfer to me.

My most important role was to take very good care of Mrs. DV throughout her hospitalization. I was dedicated and passionate. I did my very best. Mrs. DV's surgery was a great success, and the complex parathyroid tumors that permeated the vast tissue of her thyroid gland were removed, leaving only a small portion of one parathyroid gland behind as is the standard treatment. After Mrs. DV's operation and during her recovery, I was at her bedside almost continuously to be certain she had everything she needed and making sure I was living up to, and exceeding, the expectations of my Surgical Chief. In taking care of Mrs. DV—my very first patient as a surgical intern—I found purpose, and it was rewarding. In the hours spent caring for her, I learned about her family, about the loss of her husband, about the things she liked to do, and about the things that brought joy to her life. Mrs. DV was my first patient *as a "real doctor," and I was proud to know she was recovering and doing well because of my work. Mrs. DV was happy to see me when I came in to check on her, and through a carefully curated network of nurses, fellow interns, and medical students, I ensured she had all she needed, even when I wasn't in the hospital.*

Unexpectedly, my great care of Ms. DV would lead to a grand life purpose and ultimately change my life forever.

Mrs. DV's hospital course was uneventful, and ultimately, my first patient as a "doctor," was discharged home.

Weeks later, I would learn Mrs. DV had a daughter, and her daughter had a best friend. Mrs. DV's daughter's best friend was a nurse and worked in the hospital. After leaving the hospital, Mrs. DV shared her positive hospital experience with her daughter. Mrs. DV also told her daughter's friend, the nurse, that she met "a most wonderful doctor" during her hospitalization who happened to be "handsome and available." Mrs. DV's daughter's friend, the nurse, became my wife, mother to my son and daughter, and my love of a lifetime.

Personalization

Compassion heals. Personalized care embodies the essential tenets that Hippocrates and other healers espoused. A real connection exists between the mind, body, and spirit. When Hippocrates diagnosed Nikias, he found that his body was out of balance. So, Hippocrates delved into Nikias' life. He discovered that Nikias was stressed and working too hard in his business. From physical symptoms, he knew that Nikias had blockages. As a gifted physician, Hippocrates was able to connect Nikias' history with the physical elements of his examination to diagnose Nikias' failing heart. Hippocrates personalized Nikias' care. He treated him as an individual.

Hippocrates also took care of poor people. This fact serves as an indication of his high moral character. Because he did not prioritize money, we get a sense of where his heart was. He also had the compassion to help someone like Nikias, who had the means to get help but, because he did not receive the right help, collapsed. These characteristics—compassion, personalized care, and personalized treatment—exemplify the true healer. Something special about Hippocrates' spirit and demeanor almost instantly inspired trust in those he treated. These are also characteristics a healer needs. Simply being a great technician does not inspire a patient's trust or engender confidence. Many skills must come together. Historical references to Hippocrates suggest he brought these many ideals together to bear on each of his cases. Many physicians still take the Hippocratic oath to reinforce these ideals as being those they want to embody as a professional healer. As healers, restoring an individual's body, mind, and spirit is our greatest work. From 399 BC to the present day, we have seen many noteworthy variations of the great Hippocratic healer.

Ideally, reflecting on the past brings us back to the present with improved perspective. Even though we've moved beyond dogs, snakes, and leeches to molecular genetics, artificial intelligence, and precision medicine that measures human parameters in great detail, we can never forget how much we gain by being healers and all that encompasses. A textbook cannot teach the ability to heal effectively. Learning to heal comes from actually doing the work as a care provider who inspires trust.

THE ART OF HUMAN CARE
IN ACTION

Personalization:
Unbiased Care

"Good luck, Dr. Tetteh!" the nurse exclaimed as I was about to enter the preoperative room she had just left. We'd worked together for months. She was an excellent nurse, and I never recalled her displaying stress in any situation. Yet, whatever was behind that door had struck a nerve.

"Good luck?" I looked at her with puzzlement, and she shook her head as she walked away.

This nurse worked in the preoperative surgical suite and compassionately cared for many of my patients before they went in for elective heart surgery. She was an affable African-American woman with beautiful locks of hair, a magnanimous spirit, and an infectious smile, and she was completely dedicated to her patients. Each day she meticulously reviewed all of the

preoperative paperwork and ensured all of the patient's and the family's questions were answered. She also took extra care to make sure the patient and family's anxiety, fears, and concerns were addressed before she let the doctors come in to talk about the surgery at hand. Her work made our jobs easier, and our patients entered the operating rooms at ease and with assurance that they would be well cared for.

On this particular occasion, I was prepared to answer any last-minute questions before our patient was to receive a new heart valve. At this point in my career, I had recently completed my thoracic surgery fellowship in Minnesota and was now a senior cardiac surgery fellow at a prestigious hospital in Boston that was affiliated with Harvard Medical School. It was an honor, and I pinched myself every day to make sure I wasn't dreaming about being in such a fortunate position. Enduring five years of an intense general surgery residency after four years of medical school, two years of active practice in the Navy as a surgeon with a deployment around the world, and three long grueling years in Minnesota had honed my skills as a thoracic surgeon and brought me to this point. This was an opportunity to learn even more and to refine my craft as a heart surgeon and senior cardiac fellow working among the best heart surgeons in the world.

When my exasperated nurse left the patient's room, however, I did not think about all of my training, the many cases like this I'd had before, or how I came to be in my position. None of these things mattered now. In this moment, the only thing that mattered was how I would take care of the patient behind the door — the patient who had upset the nurse. I knew a challenge faced me. I put myself in a happy mood, as I always did when greeting patients. Heart patients are understandably filled with great anxiety, fear, and concern. As in the past, I placed myself in the patient's shoes and walked into her room.

"Well, first I had Whoopi and now I have Tiger," said Mrs. BB, associating me with the African American golfer Tiger Woods. Mrs. BB was the patient, and her greeting struck me hard. Her bias was palpable. Upon entering the room, her first comment was to immediately comment on the African American nurse who had just left the room and then to refer to me as "Tiger." Over the years, despite being their physician and surgeon, patients often mistook me for the television repairman, housekeeping staff, a tech, or a nurse. Never before was I called Tiger Woods, and it was not the greeting I expected. However, I defaulted to my maxim and placed myself in the shoes of the patient before me. Mrs. BB was an elderly white woman who spent most of her life, undoubtedly, in the suburbs of Boston. She had an aura of wealth and privilege, even dressed in her unflattering hospital gown. Her affluence was augmented by her bespoken spouse, seated cross-legged in the chair next to her hospital bed. Mrs. BB's husband wore a finely tailored tweed jacket, exhibited a meticulously tied bowtie, and had spectacles perched on the brim of his nose. He looked ever-so-slightly over those glasses while he read the paper, only briefly interrupting his gaze at the periodical to look at me.

He glanced at me and then at his wife before Mrs. BB questioned, "Where are your golf clubs?" Again, I was struck by the comment, shocked and disturbed by her question. I understood fully why the nurse had exited the room in exasperation only to wish me luck before I entered Mrs. BB's room.

I said good morning and informed Mrs. BB that I was one of the surgeons on the team caring for her. I emitted a cordial, respectful smile. Without a moment's hesitation, she asked if the "real surgeon" was going to be in the operating room during her procedure.

I assured her that real surgeons were on her case and proceeded to explain in great detail our planned procedure for repairing her mitral heart valve. She appeared to be both dubious and happy when I left the room. As I made my way out, I imagined how anxious she must be. The woman was about to undergo open heart surgery, and yet she continued to spew a barrage of insensitive and biased remarks aimed at the one individual who had expressed that his one important role was to help her through her surgical procedure and hospitalization. I couldn't understand.

My team and I proceeded to take Mrs. BB to the operating room. We repaired her valve, and she had an uneventful immediate operative and postoperative course.

Later that afternoon, while she was in the ICU recovering, I was making my rounds. Mrs. BB was waking up and almost fully alert. Yet she still had an uncomfortable breathing tube in her throat. The ICU nurse caring for Mrs. BB asked me if it was time for her

to be extubated and to have her breathing tube removed. I could tell Mrs. BB understood her situation as she looked at me. I could sense her discomfort and then, as her eyes adjusted on me, I imagined that Mrs. BB reflected deeply on her treatment of me earlier in the day—at least I wanted to think so. I provided the order for the ICU nurse to remove Mrs. BB's breathing tube, ease her discomfort, and ensure she was comfortable despite how uncomfortable she'd made both me and my nursing colleague just a few hours earlier.

What I realized on that day, and on so many other occasions, was one simple truth. Personalization of one's care and placing yourself in the patient's shoes is an important attribute of human care, even when a patient doesn't much care for the idea of you being their physician or surgeon because of the color of your skin.

Partnership

What is the difference between human care and health care? The difference lies in the scope of perspective, appreciating more than the obvious disease, illness, or injury a patient presents. It requires the ability to look beyond medicine alone. Human care is much more comprehensive and encompassing than health care. It's more than medicine and operations. It requires us to look at the whole world around the patient and everything impacting their health. Only then can we make them better. Ultimately, human care requires a partnership. Do patients have the resources to become healthy? Safe neighborhoods to ride a bike? Good grocery stores? Can the patient do the things we assume they need to do in order to get better? The provider needs to create a partnership with the patient, as well as with the care team, patient's family, and patient's community in order to address individual needs and restore health.

When the key elements of purpose, personalization, and partnerships combine, the resulting product is human care. When physicians apply the art of human care, the results not only change the patient's life but also change the world.

Partnership:
How a Team Rallies Together
to Save a Life

Mr. PF was an amazing patient—one of those patients where routine turns into something much more eventful. I came to meet him much like my many other patients, through consultation with cardiology. Mr. PF needed a very simple straightforward four-vessel coronary artery bypass grafting (CABG) for occluded heart vessels. He was a pleasant, otherwise healthy man with a history of heart disease that was very typical. Mr. PF's case became an atypical event intraoperatively after the conclusion of our surgical case.

We preoperatively assessed Mr. PF and took care of him much like all of our other patients. Like many cases before Mr. PF, we expected all to progress very well without any complication.

Throughout the procedure, there were no signs or indication that his case would be any different.

However, one learns quickly that, at times, the only thing certain in cardiac surgery may be uncertainty.

After completing all of our bypass grafts on a very short bypass pump run—while attempting to wean Mr. PF from the cardiopulmonary heart-lung bypass machine—his heart failed to perform. In fact, he would not come off the bypass machine. With each attempt, we checked all of our grafts to ensure everything was okay. Indeed, everything was fine. Yet, for some reason, Mr. PF's heart was not performing. He was dying.

Something is terribly wrong when patients fail to come off of the bypass machine, especially in an otherwise healthy patient. A series of thoughts goes through a surgeon's mind. Quick critical thinking and action are the only ways to address the issue. It was during this thoughtful exercise in the middle of Mr. PF's crisis that I realized how a partnership forged months earlier could mean everything to save his life.

Months prior to this case, I had walked into an operating room as the attending surgeon and was greeted as the housekeeping staff by the senior nurse in the room. A series of responses went through my mind including: "Do I look like housekeeping?" "Is it because I'm black?" "Is it because I'm male?" "Is it because I'm dressed like a housekeeper?" I reserved all of those thoughts, however, and simply told her, "No, I'm not housekeeping." I calmly corrected her and informed her that I was, in fact, Dr. Tetteh, the attending surgeon, and was checking in to ensure everything was prepared for one of my first cases at the new hospital.

Now, months later, my patient Mr. PF was on the operating room table dying. We were running out of options in a hospital with very little capability beyond surgery for patients with heart failure. Yet in another hospital nearby, we had a lot of capability, and my experience provided a plethora of tools to take care of patients with the very condition Mr. PF was now experiencing postoperatively. His poorly functioning heart could be treated temporarily with an assist device that would buy us time while his heart recovered. Options existed to bridge the recovery of Mr. PF's heart, safely get him out of the operating room and hopefully to a place of recovery. The problem was that this hospital did not have that capability, and we were running out of time. I quickly communicated the problems and challenges that faced us with the entire team. I enlisted the help of others to assist and quickly devise a plan to save Mr. PF's life. I suggested we travel to the nearby hospital and get the needed equipment to help support Mr. PF.

We needed to bring the equipment back to our hospital so we could provide the life support to Mr. PF and give him the best possible chance of recovery. We developed a partnership in a time of crisis, and the team rallied. We were able to get what we needed to support Mr. PF and to get him out of the operating room on temporary support until his heart fully recovered.

In the end, it was the same nurse who had mistaken me for house-keeping staff a few months earlier who played a critical and pivotal role in the entire operation. We were able to secure the necessary equipment we needed at a time when minutes where crucial.

Mr. PF's life was saved. When he was eventually discharged, he was doing a little bit better.

I saw Mr. PF again more than two years after his heart surgery case. He relocated to Florida and was visiting the hospital to see orthopedics. He'd broken a hip after being struck by a car while riding his bike. It was good to know Mr. PF's heart recovered, was still working well, and he was living an active life again.

In reflection, I was most pleased to recognize the power of partnerships, especially in moments of great crisis. Together, we shine brightly and embody the art of human care.

PEOPLE'S PASSIONS: Jessica Legon

Part III

A Call to Action:
How to Change the World
One Patient at a Time

What does the story of Nikias have to do with physicians today? In Part II, I introduced *The Art of Human Care* and its three guiding principles: purpose, personalization, and partnerships. Within this theory, I shared the story of Hippocrates' patient, Nikias. He will make his reappearance again soon. His story serves as an analogy for what happens when physicians practice human care rather than health care— they find passion. Providers who have found their purpose treat their patients as persons, not medical conditions. They build partnerships with their patients and their patients' families and communities. This revives their healing passion. Furthermore, those who are already passionate about healing become even more passionate.

The First Part of Human Care:
FINDING PURPOSE

Physicians should never underestimate their capacity to dramatically impact the lives of their patients—and consequently change the world. As I mentioned in the Introduction, a newly found purpose—to be a healer—helped me overcome a near-death illness as an undergrad.

In the days before being released from my weeks-long hospitalization, the attending emergency department doctor, who took care of me the day I was admitted, visited me. His name was Dr. McCullom. My friends had told him that I wanted to be a doctor.

Dr. McCullom presented me a copy of Harrison's *Principles of Internal Medicine*. He showed me what kind of infection I had, bacterial meningitis. Together, we read about how serious the condition was and how it could have taken my life. He also told me that since I wanted to be a doctor, he had a test for me. He proceeded to ask me, "What is two plus two?" I answered, "Four." He chuckled and said, "You will make a great doctor."

More than 20 years have passed. Yet I remember that ordeal as if it was yesterday. I also remember Dr. McCullom with gratitude for the great care he took to heal me. He helped me realize my purpose. That purpose not only spared a kid from Brooklyn from deadly meningitis but also inspired him to become a doctor who would, in time, be invited by other physicians to talk about human care. Thank you, Dr. McCullom for saving my life so I could help change the world.

My experience as an intensive care unit patient also taught me about empathy, what it feels like to be a patient.

As I mentioned, the average physician has approximately 80,000 to 100,000 patient encounters over a typical career. Dr. McCullom has, potentially, 100,000 stories similar to mine—stories that demonstrate the positive impact that their encounter with him had on their lives.

Even brief encounters that seem inconsequential at the time can have great impact on a patient's life. In my own comparatively short career, I've had opportunity to help patients discover their purpose with the smallest effort. Long before I became a doctor, a former professor took an interest in my career. He encouraged me to apply to the Harvard Kennedy School. I lost touch with him for years. In 2008, when I found myself studying at the Kennedy School and working at the Brigham and Women's Hospital in Boston, I reached out to him. It was then that I learned he had been diagnosed with advanced kidney cancer.

When we talked, he was desperate. The disease had spread to his lungs. He needed a referral for a thoracic surgeon close to where he was living and had difficulty obtaining the consult.

I was able to introduce him to a surgical colleague practicing in his area. He received excellent care. Eight years later, he was still alive. During those eight years, he lived with great purpose, with the realization that each day was a gift. He accomplished much. He wrote a book, became a popular speaker sharing his experience with other cancer survivors, and enjoyed watching his grandchildren grow up. He was alive to see the university library dedicate its new wing to him. Just as he had contributed to my career as a physician, I was able to contribute, in a small way, to helping him achieve greater purpose in his life.

Through experiences like these and years of clinical experience, I've learned that one does not have to cure in order to heal. I realize that the work physicians do in this great profession gives them an incredible power, an amazing gift, to impact the lives of others in many meaningful ways. During their routine encounters, they may never fully appreciate the magnitude of that impact.

Restoring health is an awesome purpose. Remember, Herophilus of Chalcedon, physician to Alexander the Great, observed, "When health is absent, wisdom cannot reveal itself, art cannot manifest, strength cannot fight, wealth becomes useless, and intelligence cannot be applied."

When physicians work to restore their patients' health, they can also help those patients realize their purpose. That is how physicians change the world for the better. Doctors impact the lives of millions of people through the work they do. They help mothers, fathers, teachers, children, the rich, and the poor. They help restore health so their patient's wisdom reveals itself, so art becomes manifested, so they have strength to fight, so their wealth becomes useful, so they may apply their intelligence, and so they will see their grandchildren grow up and achieve purpose, become doctors, and pass on the legacy to subsequent generations.

Purpose:
The Healing Effect
of a Smile

One does not have to cure in order to heal. During the intense and high-paced course of my thoracic surgery fellowship training in Minnesota, I routinely cared for very sick patients. The work exacted a toll, both emotionally and physically. The daily grind of seeing patients with serious, often life-threatening heart and lung conditions was challenging and difficult, not only because many of my patients were so sick but because they were so sad and often depressed. In some cases, the patients had very little hope because their condition and stage of the disease was too advanced to be reversed and beyond cure. Not uncommonly, I cared for patients who were critically ill, suffering from infections or other devastating complications of their underlying disease—usually advanced cancer.

Mr. JB was one of my patients. He had an advanced lung cancer that did not respond to aggressive treatment. Mr. JB's tumor was not amenable to surgery and actually grew while he was being treated with chemotherapy and radiation. Eventually, his tumor eroded through the chest wall. The cancer disintegrated bone, attacked his muscles, and melted his skin to protrude through his chest wall. Remarkably, Mr. JB was able to breathe on his own without the use of machine assistance. With every breath he took, there was obvious discomfort. To complicate matters, the chemotherapy and radiation he received delayed his wound healing and made him susceptible to infections. Regrettably, the tissue damage from many radiation treatments and the poisonous chemotherapy had not done much to curtail the advancement of Mr. JB's cancer, but it had done much to leave him in a state of despair and in a desperate condition.

Every day, my team and I would come in to change his dressings. It was a painful ritual and an excruciatingly difficult experience for us—even more so for Mr. JB. We gave him medication to ease his pain, but he winced with every movement as we pulled bandages away during the dressing changes. You could feel his pain. He never smiled. He never laughed. He was always sad. Mr. JB knew his end was near and that perhaps what we were doing on a daily basis was simply extending the inevitable. The whole exercise elicited a hopeless feeling at times, and yet, every day, we repeated the routine, hoping one day it would come to an end for both of us.

Then, one day I realized a truth that was often lost in the day-to-day routine of my busy thoracic surgery practice. Yes, indeed, it was true that our patient, Mr. JB, had limited days with us and was going to die. In fact, the truth was that we were all going to die—eventually. I was, therefore, going to adjust my outlook. On that day, I went into Mr. JB's room with a different perspective. I was determined to ensure that Mr. JB would have a different kind of day. I wanted to make sure he would think of something besides his condition, being in the hospital, painful dressing changes, and the limited days ahead. I took the time to learn a bit of his life history before his advanced cancer diagnosis. This was all I needed. My team and I set our material up just as we'd always done, but this time there was one big difference. I evoked a memory he had shared upon his admission, recalled our fallibility as surgeons, and said something to him that made him smile. Mr. JB's smile almost elicited a chuckle. It was amazing to behold. In that moment, I realized the great power we have as care providers—an ability to heal the spirit for a fleeting moment, even without curing the body.

The Second Part of Human Care:
MAKING IT PERSONAL

It is very difficult to apply statistics to a single patient. While our knowledge is extraordinarily precise for predicting what would happen to 1,000 patients with a certain condition, as the denominator becomes smaller, accuracy in prediction attenuates exponentially. This inaccuracy especially rings true when a doctor sees a patient who does not fit the statistical model. My patients have taught me how important it is to personalize an encounter, personalize communication, personalize instructions, and, most importantly, personalize care. Human care means personalization—delivering the right care to the right patient at the right time.

Physicians who want to practice human care exemplify its components, especially the principle of personalization, by:

- Taking care of patients as individuals.
- Impacting patients' lives in a positive way.
- Partnering with their colleagues, hospitals, and medical societies, and at times local, state, and federal government to improve the care of their patients.
- Maximizing patient encounters—they connect with their patients, develop relationships, leverage interactions to benefit the patient, shape the conversation, and make the most of each doctor/patient engagement.
- In their own way, exemplifying the "power of the visit," recognizing that this is what, in part, brings success.

This is how, when physicians provide human care, they change the world.

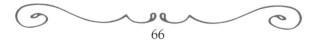

Personalization:
Never Underestimate the Potential
of Your Patients

There are some patients you never forget. Despite caring for hundreds of people and visiting with thousands of patients and their families, there are some who leave a mark on your heart. Mrs. WB was one of those special patients.

I met Mrs. WB in an untraditional way. Although I was not on call that late Friday afternoon, I received a phone call from a consulting cardiologist.

The patient, Mrs. WB, was 88 years old, he began. Immediately upon hearing her age, I dismissed her condition as a nonsurgical case and almost entirely tuned out the rest of what he said. The cardiologist proceeded to explain that Mrs. WB was admitted with shortness of breath, fatigue, and some dizziness. All of her symptoms were determined to be related to several pathologic conditions of her heart, including a leaking mitral valve, leaking tricuspid valve, as well as an arrhythmia causing atrial fibrillation. The medical team had exhausted all medical therapies and was now consulting the cardiac surgery service.

The cardiologist ended the call by expressing that, based on her age, he did not believe Mrs. BB would be a good surgical candidate. Even before seeing the patient, I agreed. Despite the fact that I wasn't on call and it was a Friday afternoon, I informed him I would see Mrs. WB.

When I arrived at Mrs. WB's room, a petite, firecracker of a woman walked up and greeted me at the door with a strong and firm handshake. This greeting was very rare. Most often, I arrive at a patient's room only to find them lying on a bed or sitting in a chair. I am the one who approaches the patient. I think this was the very first time in my entire career that a patient walked to the door to greet me even before I crossed the threshold. Mrs. WB's grasp and shake of my hand embodied a firm confidence. She looked me directly in the eyes and said, "Are you the surgeon who is going to operate on me?"

"Well, that is definitely putting the cart before the horse," I thought. I had only just met her, and she immediately asked if I was going to be her surgeon. This very short, determined, African-American woman—with a very firm handshake—clearly did not appear to be the frail 88-year-old woman I had envisioned before meeting her.

Mrs. WB's daughter was quietly sitting in the back of the patient's room. She smiled as Mrs. WB greeted me. I introduced myself to them and explained that I would discuss some of the available treatment options with them.

Mrs. WB dismissed all other options summarily and explained that the medical team had already informed her that the medical options for treatment were exhausted. Mrs. WB said, "I'm told that because I have a leaking valve, my heart is not working well and that it needs to be fixed so I can get back to my bowling."

"Bowling?" I asked.

At that point, Mrs. WB's daughter reported that not only was Mrs. WB an avid bowler with matches several times a week, but that she also danced regularly, did yoga, and took Zumba classes.

"Wow!" I thought. "Okay, well, let's talk about surgery."

Mrs. WB did, in fact, have a severe case of mitral regurgitation as well as tricuspid regurgitation. Remarkably, her heart function was very good despite the valvular heart pathology and her arrhythmia. I later learned that Mrs. WB's cardiologist had followed her condition closely for years, deferring surgery since they knew that, even though her valves were not completely normal, she was older and was functioning well despite her valve pathology.

Now, though, in order to return Mrs. WB to her activities and doing the things that made her happy (like bowling, dancing, yoga, and Zumba), we needed to plan for surgery. Mrs. WB was the 88-year-old I wanted to be when I grew up.

After doing a thorough preoperative assessment, we took her to surgery and performed a double valve repair as well as a procedure to correct her arrhythmia. Her postoperative course was uncomplicated. She did well and, in fact, better than most patients much younger. Mrs. WB was eventually discharged, returning only a few days later to have a small amount of fluid drained from around her lungs. Mrs. WB and her daughter were both very appreciative. I learned in that moment that personalizing care to the patient you meet, not to a chronologic number of age, was what was best and most prudent.

Years after her surgery, I would see Mrs. WB again. She was 95 years old and was in a wheelchair—not because she couldn't walk but only because it was a long way from the parking lot to the clinic at the hospital. Mrs. WB was there to get an annual checkup and an echocardiogram to evaluate her heart. Mrs. WB smiled warmly when she saw me. Her daughter gave me a hug.

In reflection, I was very happy to have received that consult on a Friday afternoon when I was not on call. I thought how thoroughly Mrs. WB's case had embodied personalization and the art of human care.

The Third Part of Human Care:
SYNERGY of PARTNERSHIP

Partnerships make the impossible possible. I saw this truth become evident when I served with the Navy in Afghanistan. Thanks to service partnerships among the Army, Navy, Marines, and Air Force, I saw the impossible become possible every day. I saw the impossible work of saving lives in a tent under poor conditions. I saw the impossible work of returning mortally injured warriors home to loved ones just hours after an injury. One act, one decision by one person—or the synergy of a team working together—saved a generation of young lives.

Changing the world can happen anywhere. Any individual can do it. In the realm of medicine, it starts here, today, with human care. Human care revives a physician's passion and will, indeed, change the world.

I enjoy sharing this story that captures the impact of partnerships. While I was serving at the Congressional Budget Office (CBO) as Visiting Scholar and clinical advisor to the health economists and policy experts, one of my colleagues mentioned that his high school daughter was interested in being a physician. I invited him and his daughter to visit the hospital operating room's observation dome to witness open-heart surgery.

A seasoned career health economist, my CBO colleague had limited experience with health care beyond regular check-ups and an occasional emergency room visit. He had neither witnessed a surgery nor had opportunity to appreciate first-hand the resource-intensive environment of an operating room suite.

As soon as the case started, his daughter began watching with keen interest. However, my colleague immediately put on his health economist's "hat." He critically inquired, "Why are there so many people in the operating room not doing anything?" Recognizing that he was new to the operating room experience, I simply asked him to have patience, reserve his judgment of the inactive staff, and carefully watch the operation. I assured him that eventually he would appreciate how everyone on the team contributed and performed throughout the procedure.

Indeed, it was a great suggestion. As my colleague carefully studied the operation, he began to realize how much human and capital resources were necessary to provide the patient a safe environment and to perform a complex procedure that opened the patient's chest and stopped his heart.

After the surgery, my colleague had one emphatic word: "Wow!" The experience forever changed both him and his daughter. For the first time in his full career as a seasoned health economist, he had observed health care and its associated costs through a different lens and with a fresh perspective.

What began as a simple gesture to provide an interested teenager a glimpse of my world of medicine had evolved into a learning partnership. My colleague shared his experience with others at the CBO. Soon after, many other CBO staff visited our hospital dome to observe surgeries. It's likely that consequently, their experience influenced their perspective on health care costs. While I learned about the federal budget process and economic models, my CBO colleagues learned more about the clinical demands of health care delivery.

Ultimately, throughout late 2013, members of the Budget Analysis Division (BAD) also visited surgeries, along with more senior CBO officials. The BAD was responsible for rescoring the Sustainable Growth Rate (SGR) equation, achieving a solution that ultimately led to a negotiated agreement that facilitated the Medicare/Medicaid reimbursements "doc fix" and the costly budgetary offsets for the SGR to be adjudicated.

MENTORS: Jessica Legon

THE ART OF HUMAN CARE
IN ACTION

Partnership:
A Miracle in the Desert

"You want me to do what?"

"Yes, we need you to fly across the desert to our other hospital. We have a patient waiting for you—a baby who was shot in the heart."

That was the call I received just before hearing another ominous sound—the sound of helicopters coming for me. I was in the middle of the Afghanistan desert on my deployment as a combat trauma surgeon and was called by the large receiving hospital to come and operate on a baby Afghan child who had been shot in the heart.

The entire case was unusual. Seldom does anyone have time to make a consultation or call when a patient has been shot in the heart. The baby's misfortune, or perhaps luck, depending on one's perspective, was that the bullet fragment had pierced the infant's arm, and the defrayed fragments of the bullet went through the baby's arm and penetrated the child's chest and heart. Indeed, the diverted course of the bullet fragments were the only reason the child survived long enough to make it to the operating room.

It was in the operating room, while the other surgeons were taking care of the patient's other injuries, where I met Baby M. During this particular deployment, I was the only thoracic surgeon in the area. We were dispersed throughout the Helmand province of Afghanistan taking care of our wounded warriors when I was called to care for the baby and address the bullet fragment in the child's chest. It was nestled in the heart, causing the baby to be unstable and creating a dire life and death situation for Baby M.

This was a different kind of case. This was an injured Afghan child. To say that I was anxious would be an understatement. I knew I would have to fly by helicopter, through a war zone, to get to the other hospital where Baby M was waiting. I also knew there was great risk involved in ensuring survival for the baby. Every bit of my clinical and surgical trauma experience suggested the baby had little chance of survival, especially since it would take me some time to get to the hospital. Even upon arrival, I imagined limited options to help. It seemed impossible.

Our success would require the partnership and cooperation of many. When I arrived at the hospital, Baby M was already in the operating room with the team waiting for me. I was on the spot. It was an intense time and an intense moment. Baby M was so small, and the baby's vital signs were not stable. I reviewed the images and the bullet fragment's proximity to his heart. The baby's survival defied logic. Without the technology and many of the amenities *we had in America to perform heart surgery, Baby M's case was going to be very challenging. No heart lung bypass machine. No way to support Baby M's blood pressure if massive bleeding was encountered.*

We proceeded. With great trepidation, I opened the baby's chest and relieved the bleeding around the infant's heart that was causing Baby's M's instability. The case was a success.

We succeeded because of partnerships. We made the impossible possible because of the team that worked together. It was the partnership of the helicopter pilots, my surgical and anesthesia colleagues, and a very capable cohort of nurses and physicians at the hospital who saved Baby M's life after being shot in the heart. Our partnership embodied the art of human care. Partnership made the impossible possible. It saved Baby M and created a miracle in the desert.

The Art of Human Care

So, what does the story of Nikias have to do with all of this? The answer can be found in *The Art of Human Care*. Like Hippocrates, applying the principles of purpose, personalization, and partnerships restores health.

The Art of Human Care reveals purpose, personalization, and partnerships through its practice and compassion for others. It is not enough to know about the power of art; we must apply art's power to our work of healing and restoring health. It is not enough to be willing to do the work of healing; we must heal and restore health. This art is long, requires effort, and transcends the short life we have on earth.

Human care advances health. With health, wisdom reveals itself, art becomes manifest, we have strength to fight life's challenges, our wealth becomes useful, and we may apply our intelligence and positively change the world for generations. Let us apply the art. Let us do the work.

DALTON SHAULL

THE BUTTERFLY EFFECT OF HEALING

Afterword

Dalton Shaull

Dr. Tetteh's book is a story of a man's ultimate pursuit of purpose and surrendering to the call of service. It bears a fruitful collection of experiences and insights that provide a renewed perspective of what it means to heal and our abilities as artists, coaches, teachers, or doctors, to transform our routine encounters into routine inspiration.

Dr. Tetteh's theory of Human Care is an art that has implications far exceeding the walls of the hospital. It reminds us that by taking the holistic approach to healing with every patient, we can set off a cascade of purpose—the ultimate butterfly effect.

About this drawing

My drawing symbolizes this "butterfly effect" of healing. I start by covering the entire page black with a mix of black charcoal and conte. Then, using subtractive or negative technique, I use an eraser to draw the organ (essentially, I erase more where I want it lighter and less where I want it darker). I then use scissors to cut the organ out closely to its edges. I do this to symbolize the practice and art of procurement and recovery.

I then place the organ on a colorful background that I paint using acrylic paints. This rather "dark" (or dead) organ is being placed into an environment full of color (or life) to symbolize the transplant and implant of a new organ into the recipient.

Finally, in this particular example, I use acrylic paint to paint in flowers coming from the veins and arteries of the heart. This is to symbolize the patient being weaned from bypass and the patient's blood now flowing through its new organ—new life.

Transplant is truly a remarkable example of not only amazing surgical skill, medical innovation, and finesse, but also the orchestration of a myriad of other components, which makes it one of the most complex and fascinating procedures in medicine. It is so fascinating to me that I have chosen to dedicate the rest of my life to working and innovating within this field. If you are receiving this drawing, it is because of my admiration for what you do to advance health and save lives. It is your passion, your pursuit of personal mastery (with your clinical/surgical skills and administration and leadership), and your determination in continually challenging the status quo. I look forward to working with you on our shared mission of saving lives for many years to come. Thank you.

Acknowledgments

First, this book would not exist without the service, care, sacrifice, and compassion of all who have cared for another human. I am especially thankful to those who work every day in our places of healing to do the hard work of restoring health and wellness. These individuals deserve all the honor.

I am indebted to the many patients I have met over the years, for they provide inspiration and wisdom. Stories and drama connect more effectively with people than facts and random words. Thus, the story of Nikias and Hippocrates was adapted from a book called *The Sublime Engine: A Biography of the Human Heart,* by brothers Stephen and Thomas Amidon. The story resonated with me because I visited the Healing Temple of Asclepius in Kos, Greece, referenced in the story long before I read their book.

My teachers, mentors, and coaches have directly and indirectly influenced this work and taught the healing art of medicine and surgery. The conceptual, editorial, and artistic work of Juanell Teague, Karen Brownlee, Karen McDiarmid, Jessica Legon, Dick Bruso, Dalton Shaull, William Maples, Jack Canfield, Jeff Gusky, and Steven Dana was invaluable.

Finally, the most thanks must go to my family—Isabel, Viviana, and especially my wife Lisa, son Edmund, and daughter Ella—for tolerating and supporting both a surgeon's and an author's schedule. Thank you all for always listening at the kitchen table to endless recitals, for enduring many drafts and revisions, and for your patience, love, and support with tea, a special treat, and warm embrace through many days and long nights. You are all a blessing I am very lucky to have you and thank God for you every day.

Hic Pro Bonus
Here for Good...
Hassan A. Tetteh MD
Baltimore, Maryland

· ·

References

Hippocrates (2012). *Hippocrates Aphorismi* (Latin edition). San Bernardino, CA: Ulan Press.

Amidon, S., and Amidon, T. (2011). *The Sublime Engine: A Biography of the Human Heart.* Emmaus, PA: Rodale Books.

Herophilus, and Von Staden, Heinrich (1989). *Herophilus: The Art of Medicine in Early Alexandria.* New York: Cambridge University Press.

Frankl, Viktor E. (1992). *Man's Search for Meaning.* London: Rider Books.

Isselbacher, Kurt J., et al. (1994). *Harrison's Principles of Internal Medicine* (Thirteenth Edition). New York: McGraw-Hill Education.

Hahn, Jim (2012). "Medicare Physician Payment Updates and the Sustainable Growth Rate (SGR) System." *Congressional Research Service.*

Isaacson, Walter (2017). *Leonardo da Vinci.* New York: Simon and Schuster.

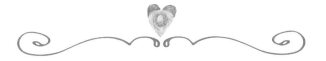

Dr. Hassan A. Tetteh

Photo by Angie Vasquez

Dr. Hassan A. Tetteh is a US Navy Captain and Associate Professor of Surgery at the Uniformed Services University of the Health Sciences and adjunct faculty at Howard University College of Medicine. He was a Robert Wood Johnson Health Policy Fellow from 2012–2013, assigned to the US Congress, Congressional Budget Office, (CBO). Currently, Tetteh is a Thoracic Surgeon for MedStar Health and Walter Reed National Military Medical Center. He leads a Specialized Thoracic Adapted Recovery (STAR) Team, in Washington, D.C., and his research in thoracic transplantation aims to expand heart and lung recovery and save lives.

A native of Brooklyn, New York, Tetteh received his BS from State University of New York (SUNY) at Plattsburgh, his MD from SUNY Downstate Medical Center, his MPA from Harvard's Kennedy School of Government, his MBA from Johns Hopkins University Carey Business

School, and his MS in National Security Strategy with a concentration in Artificial Intelligence from the National War College. He completed his thoracic surgery fellowship at the University of Minnesota and advanced cardiac surgery fellowship at Harvard Medical School's Brigham and Women's Hospital in Boston.

Tetteh is founder and principal of Tetteh Consulting Group, a best-selling author of four books, including *Gifts of the Heart, Star Patrol, The Art of Human Care,* and *Seven Pillars of Life.* Tetteh is board certified in thoracic surgery, general surgery, clinical informatics, and healthcare management, and is a Fellow of the American College of Surgeons and Fellow of the American College of Healthcare Executives.

Tetteh received the Alley Sheridan Award by the Thoracic Surgery Foundation for Research and Education, was named a TEDMED Front Line Scholar, and is a TEDx speaker. He's an alumnus of the Harvard Medical School Writers' Workshop and Yale Writers' Conference and lives near Washington, D.C., with his wife, son, and daughter.

Kudos

"Navy Captain, Dr. Hassan Tetteh, is a triple threat agent for change. He is at once a skilled cardiothoracic and combat trauma surgeon, a talented artist, and as evidenced by his authorship of *The Art of Human Care,* a passionate, caring professional with keen insight into how to begin to fix what's wrong with how we deliver healthcare today. This book is an inspirational reminder about how any one physician—how any one person, really—can change the world. I highly recommend it."

Rear Admiral David A. Lane, USN (Ret.)
Physician, Humanitarian, Mentor, Lifelong Learner, Veteran

• •

"*The Art of Human Care* reinforces—for both Physicians and their Nurse colleagues—the importance of addressing not only the physical, but also the mental and spiritual factors, to achieve true healing."

Patricia C. Seifert, MSN, RN, CNOR, CRNFA(e), FAAN
Educator, Independent Cardiac Surgery Consultant

• •

"Fate and a near-fatal event early in life often shape the commitment and perspective of a physician. Technology and science have advanced medical diagnoses and treatment. However, the best physicians master the 'Art' of medical practice. Compassion, judgment, communication and social awareness are essential elements in the "Healing Arts." This book, *The Art of Human Care,* is a must-read!"

Richard J. Shemin, MD
Robert and Kelly Day Professor and Chief, Division of Cardiac Surgery
Vice-Chairman, Department of Surgery
Co-director, Cardiovascular Center at UCLA
David Geffen School of Medicine at UCLA

"Dr. Tetteh is a renaissance leader whose brilliance is reflected from start to finish of this book. He skillfully mastered the art of storytelling, healing and teaching in one body of work.

The Art of Human Care is full of interdisciplinary wisdom and therefore a must-read for students, teachers and leaders who aspire to usher in the next wave of healthcare innovation and transformation!"

Chanté Thurmond, M.A., BSN, RYT-200
Cofounder & Cohost of The Darkest Horse

• •

"In his latest book, Dr. Tetteh brings home a clear and valuable message to the medical profession. We are not just interpreters and messengers of test results. He reminds us of our ancient history in the healing arts and of the importance of healing theory today. Presented here is a call to action for doctors to be passionate healers, empathetic listeners, and most importantly, assistants to a patient's healing and deeper purpose."

Dr. David R. Whittaker
Vascular Surgeon, Principal, Whittaker Solutions, LLC

• •

"Dr. Tetteh is a gifted healer, writer, and storyteller. In *The Art of Human Care* he weaves a beautiful tapestry of educational, inspirational and entertaining prose. He has a unique gift that takes his readers on a wonderful journey that will leave them with a renewed faith in the wonders of science and the human spirit."

C. Randall Mann
Vice President, Marketing & Public Relations, Acadian Companies

• •

"More than just a book. It combines a compelling narrative with a beautiful layout that takes you on a journey of discovery that is life-changing."

Steven Samblis
Author and Creator of 1 Habit™ book series

"An inspiring work linking Dr. Tetteh's personal life experiences with valuable lessons in becoming a thriving and resilient physician/caregiver. Changing the conversation from "What's the matter?" to "What matters most to you?" as a starting point, coupled with reflective listening, recognizing and empathetically responding to the emotions of our patients and colleagues, and creating an environment of hope, positivity, and gratitude allows physicians/caregivers to connect to their purpose—to provide health and healing to the patients and families they have the privilege of serving. *The Art of Human Care* provides a blueprint to gracefully and successfully navigate the challenging healthcare transformation which is upon us."

Dr. William Maples
President and CEO, The Institute for Healthcare Excellence

MEDICS TREE: Jessica Legon